REVISION **FUN** FOR **CLEVER** KIDS

This is **not** a workbook…but it **is** a book that works

Katie Knapman

First published in the UK in 2018 by Jumping Yak

www.jumpingyak.com

ISBN 978 1 5272 2001 0

Printed and bound in the UK by Elanders

10 9 8 7 6 5 4 3 2 1

About this Book

Do you find workbooks boring?

Do you wish learning could be fun?

Now it can be!

This book is packed with fun puzzles and tempting brain teasers for children aged 8 to 11. Everything is colour coded to help you find your way around: red for maths and logic problems, green for English, and blue for general knowledge, which includes geography, history and science.

You don't have to complete all the puzzles at once. Just dip in and out of the book when you feel like testing your wits or need a break from normal workbooks.

Everyone jumps higher with the Jumping Yak!

Words and puzzles by Katie Knapman

After graduating from Oxford University, Katie worked in television, making and presenting educational programmes for children such as *Maths 4 Real*, as well as leading prime-time shows including *Tomorrow's World* and *Countryfile*. She lives in London with her husband and two children.

Drawings by Beach

Beach has three children and two bicycles. For the rest of the time he works as an illustrator and cartoonist.

Contents

Symbolism and Colour

Colour is often used in literature to give the text more depth. If you know what different colours symbolise, you will have an even better understanding of a text. For example, Shakespeare referred to jealousy as 'the green-eyed monster'.
Use the clues below to colour in the riders. You will need the following colouring pencils: red, blue, black, yellow, purple, grey, orange, and brown.
The green one has been done for you and the white one won't need to be coloured in.

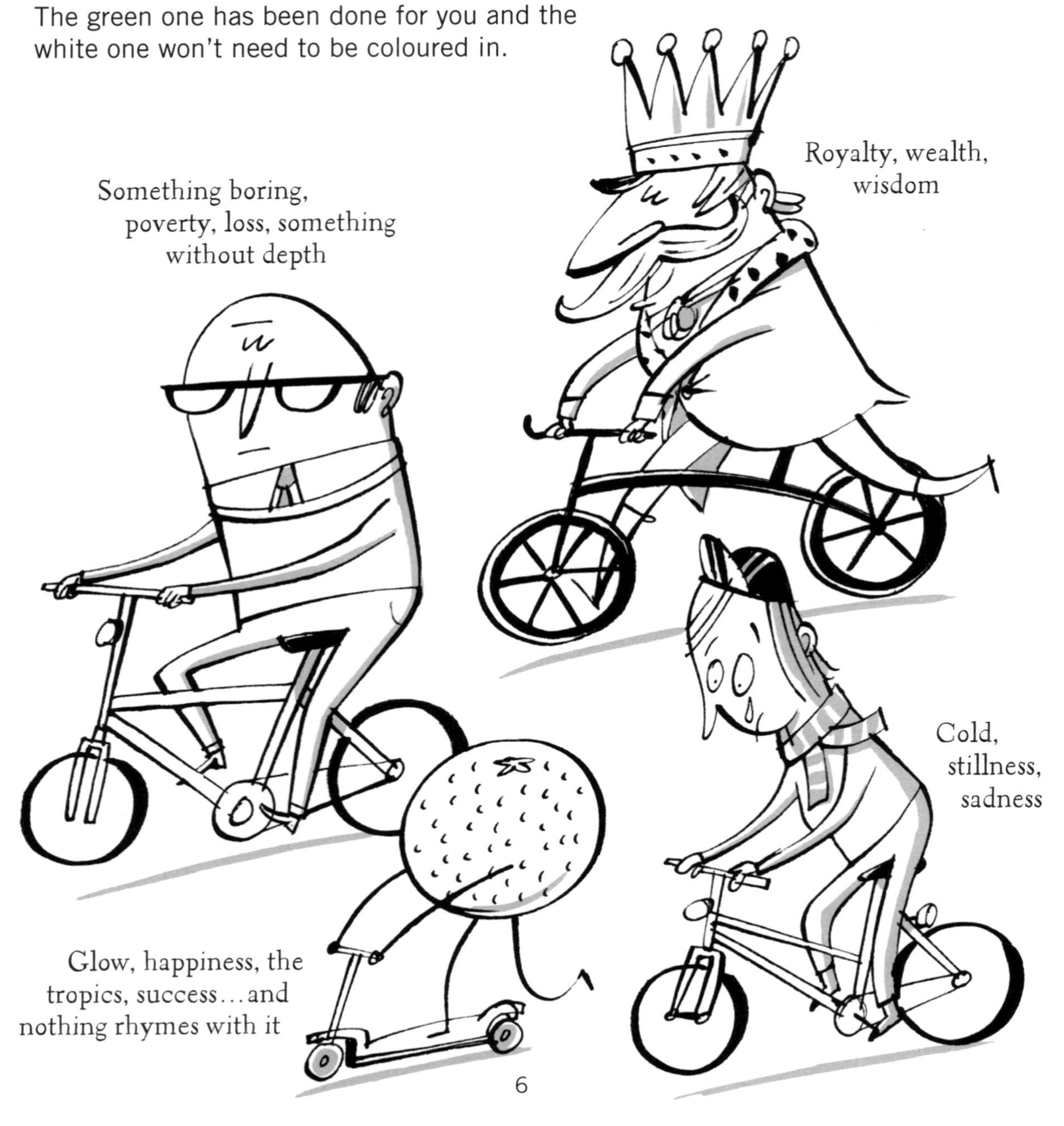

Passion, anger, violence, strength, energy, war
Purity, heaven, cleanliness, good
Sunshine and freshness…or sickness (e.g. jaundice)
Darkness, power, the unknown, mystery, or despair
Nature, new growth, jealousy, or envy
Dirt and decay, warmth, richness

What Comes Next?

Can you work out the next numbers in these sequences?

4	8	12	16	20	24	
5	10	15	20	25		
120	105	90	75	60		
1	2	4	7	11		
1	4	9	16	25		
100	94	88	82	76		
3	6	9	12	15		
3	6	11	18	27		
–10	–8	–6	–4			
5	1	–3	–7	–11		

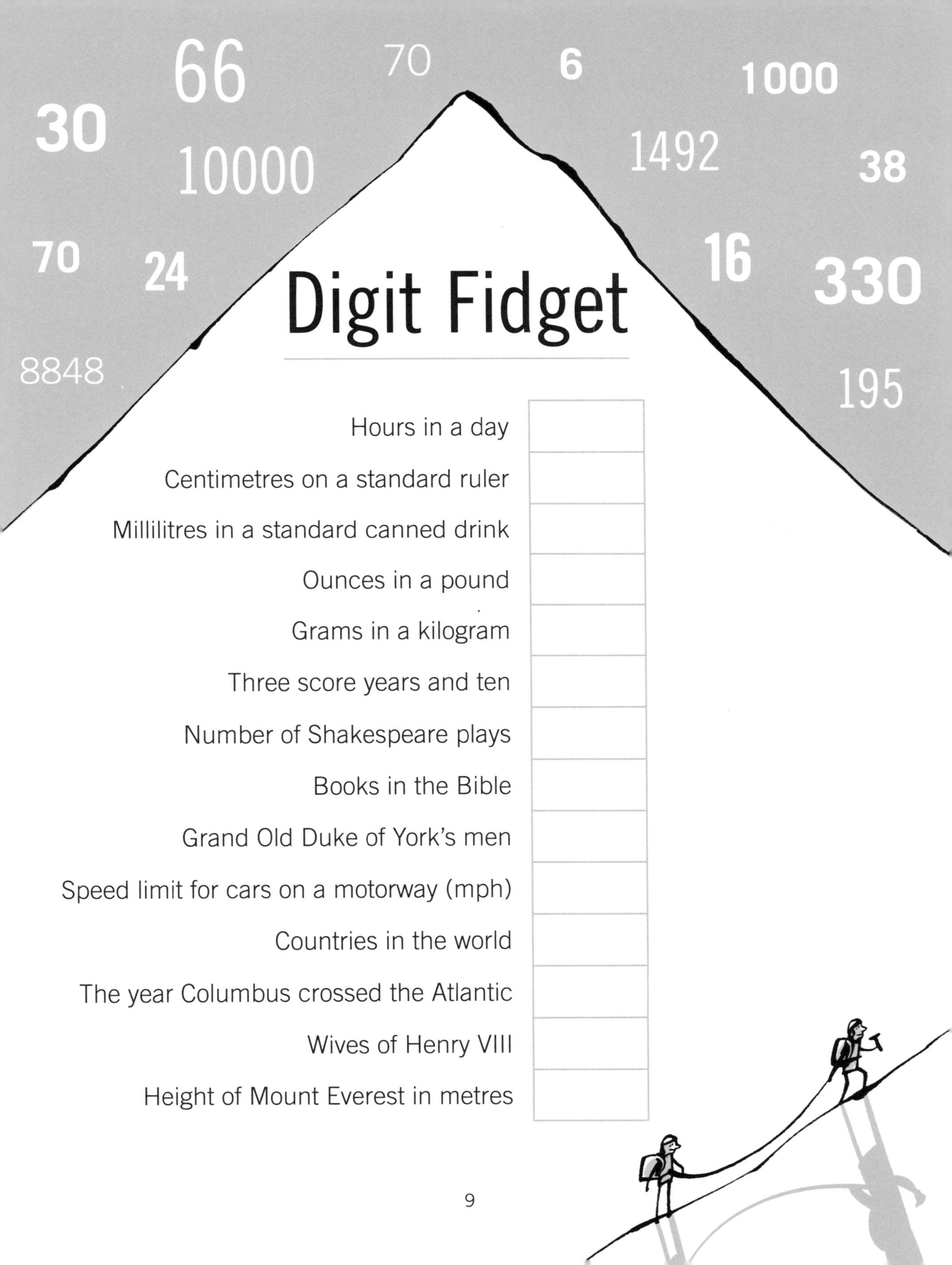

Digit Fidget

Hours in a day	
Centimetres on a standard ruler	
Millilitres in a standard canned drink	
Ounces in a pound	
Grams in a kilogram	
Three score years and ten	
Number of Shakespeare plays	
Books in the Bible	
Grand Old Duke of York's men	
Speed limit for cars on a motorway (mph)	
Countries in the world	
The year Columbus crossed the Atlantic	
Wives of Henry VIII	
Height of Mount Everest in metres	

Homophones

Homophones are words that sound the same but have different meanings, like *cereal*, eaten for breakfast, and *serial*, something that happens on a regular basis.

Can you find the homophones that fit the clues below?

R ____________ The water that falls from the sky

____________ To rule as a king or queen

L ____________ The amount of teaching given at any one time

____________ To reduce

F ____________ A crack or other imperfection

____________ The ground under your feet inside a building

N .... The dark hours between sunset and sunrise

K .... A medieval warrior of high rank usually on horseback and wearing armour

B

.... A cricketer does this when he runs towards a batsman with a ball

.... Rounded containers for food or liquid

B

.... A sleeping place on a ship or train

.... The process by which a baby comes out of its mother's body

M

.... A metal coin or cross given to someone for bravery or achievement

.... To interfere with

P

.... An agreement or treaty

.... When your suitcase is full, it is …

A .... Past tense of eat

E .... The number after seven

Who's Who?

Can you guess who these people are? The clues might help you.

English poet, playwright and actor

Also known as the Virgin Queen and Gloriana

German-born Jewish girl who wrote a diary while in hiding during WW2

Scientist famous for his theory of relativity

Civil rights leader from India

British Prime Minister 1940–1945

They were the first to the top of the world

She sat down on a bus in Alabama

Composer who became deaf

Figure It Out

Life is a bowl of cherries

The Professor, Peter, Susan, Edmund and Lucy are eating cherries. They each start with 60.

The Professor eats two-thirds of his, Peter eats 60% of his, Susan eats 45 of hers, Edmund eats half of what is in his bowl, and Lucy eats 8/15 of hers.

How many cherries does each person eat?

Who is the hungriest?

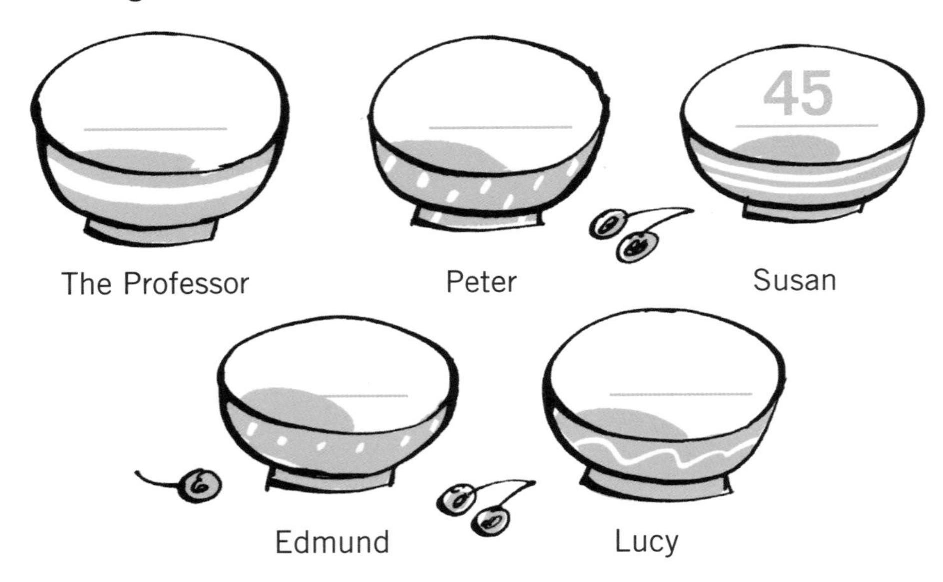

Prime Numbers

I am thinking of a prime number. When you square me,
I am three digits long. If you then reverse the last two digits,
I am still a square number. Which number am I? ________

Factors

I am the smallest number I can be with
the factors 5, 3 and 2. What am I? ________

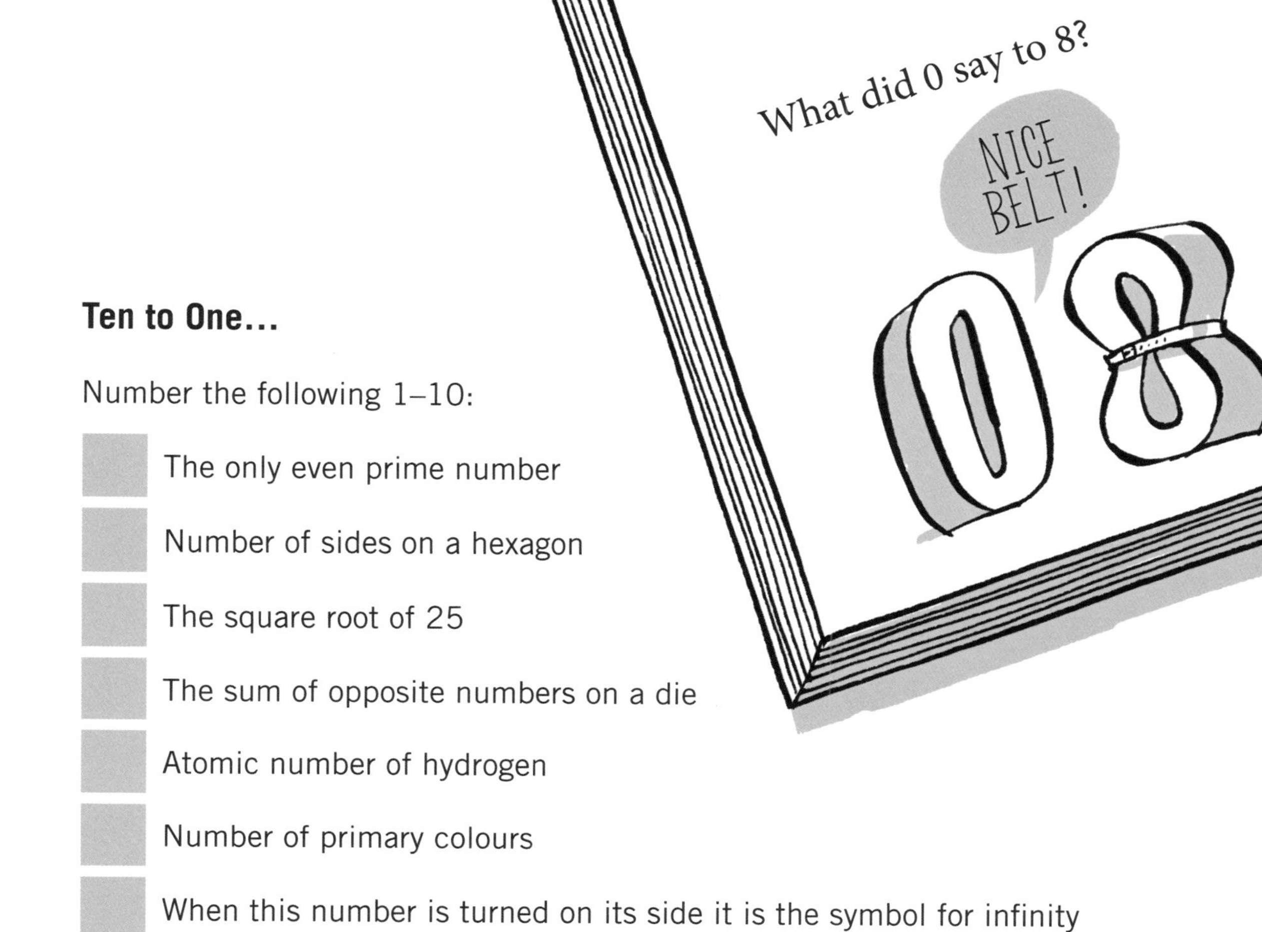

Ten to One...

Number the following 1–10:

- The only even prime number
- Number of sides on a hexagon
- The square root of 25
- The sum of opposite numbers on a die
- Atomic number of hydrogen
- Number of primary colours
- When this number is turned on its side it is the symbol for infinity
- This number is written as ‘X’ in Roman numerals
- The sum of the digits of any multiple of this number is always this number
- The only number in the English language than contains the same number of letters as its name

Why was 6 afraid of 7?

Because 7, 8, 9…

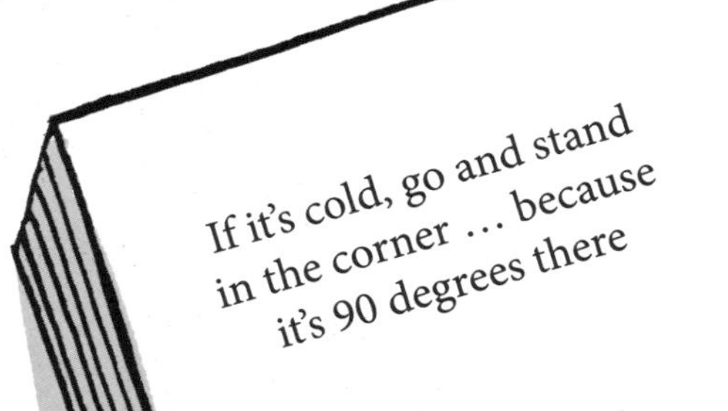

Compound Words

Find the words that will end the first word and start the second.

When you have completed the grid, the dotted squares will reveal the answer to the clue at the bottom of the page.

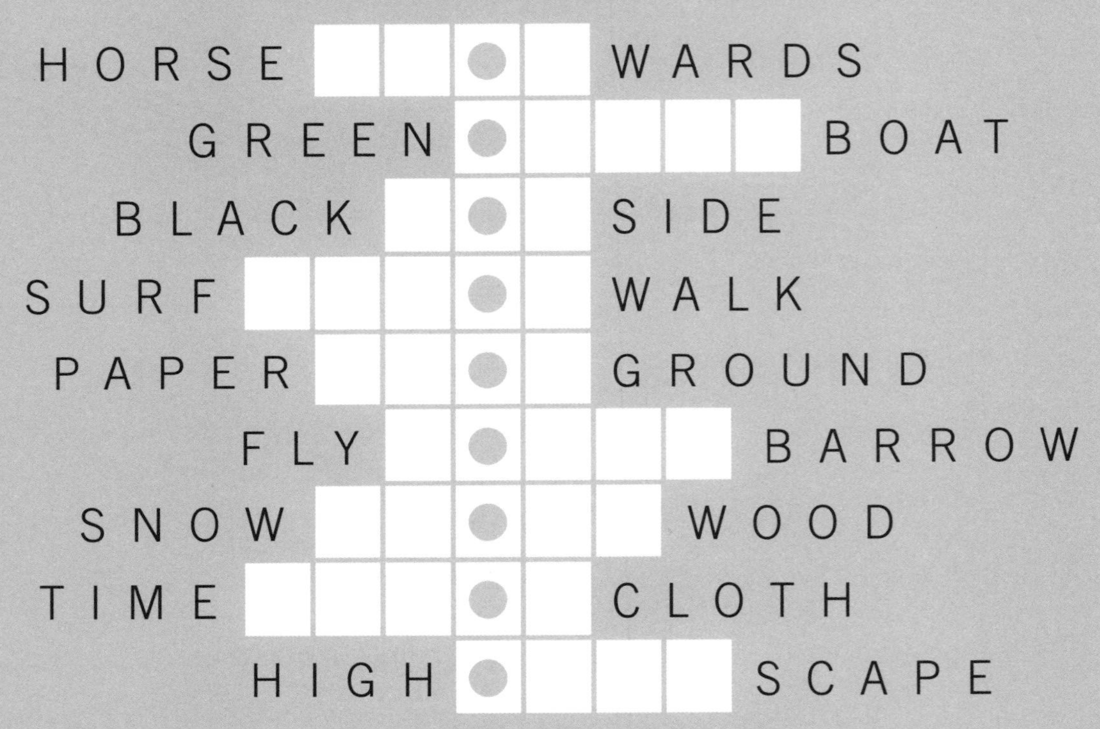

The words below come from the Greek *monos* meaning 'single' or 'alone'. Using the stem...

Mono

...can you solve this puzzle quickly before it becomes too monotonous?

A single corrective lens worn to aid vision in one eye:

A massive rock or stone:

Marriage to only one person at a time:

To have exclusive control of something; also a board game:

A railway in which the track consists of a single rail:

A long speech given by one person, often on stage to an audience:

A painting or picture in shades of one colour, or in black and white:

A word consisting of one syllable:

Science A to Z

A ______________ Greek mathematician famous for shouting 'Eureka!' in his bath

B ______________ An organ found in the head that controls many of the life processes in animals

C ______________ A physical change that takes place when a gas is cooled and changes into a liquid

D ______________ A precious stone that is the hardest natural material known on Earth

E ______________ A form of energy that can be carried by wires or stored in batteries

F ______________ Preserved remains or traces of an animal or plant that lived many years ago on Earth

G ______________ The force between two objects; on Earth it pulls us towards its core.

H ______________ An organ that pumps blood through all parts of an animal's body

I ______________ An animal without a back bone

J ______________ Where two bones meet; these allow movement in the skeleton

K ______________ Two bean-shaped organs that filter waste material from the blood

L ______________ One of the states of matter; a material that flows and takes the shape of its container

M ______________ A warm-blooded animal, usually with fur or hair, that feeds its young with milk

N ______________ A unit of force and the scientist who discovered gravity

O ______________ The curved path taken by an object as it moves around another object, e.g. the Earth around the sun

P ______________ Antibiotic discovered by Alexander Fleming in 1928

Q ______________ One of the most common materials found in the Earth's crust

R	________________	The part of a plant that holds it in the ground and takes in water
S	________________	This supports our bodies and is made up of more than 200 bones
T	________________	A see-through material which allows you to see clearly what is on the other side
U	________________	The seventh planet from the sun
V	________________	Animal with a bony skeleton and a backbone
W	________________	Also known as H_2O
X	________________	Used to detect broken bones
Y	________________	The time it takes for the Earth to go once round the sun
Z	________________	The branch of science that studies the structure, function, behaviour and evolution of animals

Bring on the Oxymorons

Oxymorons are phrases made of two words that have or seem to have opposite or different meanings. Together they create an interesting, contrasting effect. For example an **open secret** or an **honest lie**.

Circle the oxymorons below

SMART CASUAL
PAPER TOWEL
BLANK PAGE
ANNUAL LEAVE
VIRTUAL REALITY
ICED DRINK
LIVING DEAD
TALL MAN
SMART TROUSERS

WORKING HOLIDAY
PLASTIC GLASS
BITTERSWEET
DELICIOUS MEAL
WINDY DAY
DEAFENING SILENCE
HOT ICE
CHOPPY SEA
SHARP KNIFE
TIDY BEDROOM
JUMBO SHRIMP
WOOLLY SHIRT

Divisibility Rules

In maths exams and tests it is extremely useful to know quickly if one number is divisible by another number without actually doing the division. Divisibility rules are very useful here, because they help you to work out divisions quickly.

A number is divisible by...

if it is an even number

if the digits add up to a number divisible by 3

if the last two numbers are divisible by 4

if the last digit is 0 or 5

if the number is divisible by 2 and 3

if, when you multiply the last digit by 2 and subtract it from the remaining digits, the answer is divisible by 7

if the last three digits are divisible by 8

if when you add the digits the total is divisible by 9
e.g. 1,278 ... $1+2+7+8=18$ ... $1+8=9$

Now you understand divisibility rules, work out which boxes you should tick for the numbers on the left. Check your answers with a calculator.

÷	2	3	4	5
12	✓	✓	✓	
60				
183				
112				
95				
132				
340				
364				
7272				
64				

Idioms

An idiom is a word or phrase that means something different from its literal meaning. For example, if it's raining cats and dogs, it means that it's raining very hard, not that animals are falling from the sky.

There are eight idioms hidden in this picture. Can you find them and what do they really mean?

4)
5)
6)
7)
8)
CHICKENS
£20 EACH

Jumper Puzzle

In a class of children on a winter's day, three times as many wear fleeces as wear tank tops. Four more children wear gilets than tank tops. Three fewer children wear hoodies than gilets. Four children wear hoodies.

How many wear the other types of top?

Magic Squares

In these magic squares, all the rows, columns and diagonals add up to the same total. Find the magic totals and solve the squares.

8	3	
	5	
	7	

Magic Total

	1.4	0.9
	1	
1.1		

Magic Total

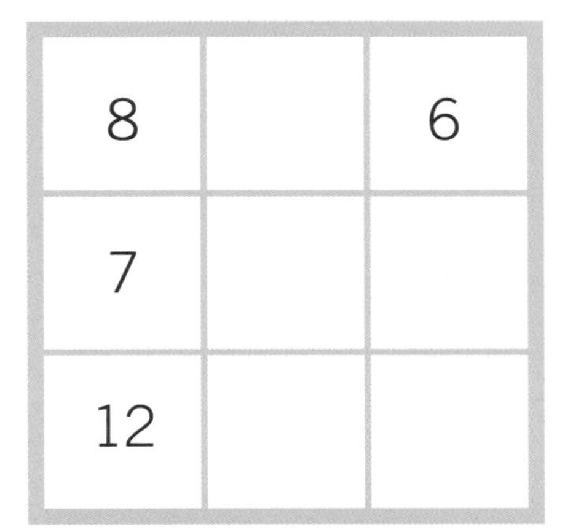

8		6
7		
12		

Magic Total

Think Laterally

Try to work out what the letters stand for in these puzzles.
The first one has been done for you.

24 H in a D ___24 Hours in a Day___

8 N in an O ______

6 W of H8 ______

48 H in 2 D ______

30 C on a R ______

52 C in a P (WJ) ______

6 is H a D ______

26 L of the A ______

7 W of the W ______

18 H on a GC ______

13 is U F S

5 T on a F

90 D in a RA

3 BM (SHTR!)

11P in a FT

360 D in a C

64 S on a CB

13 L in a BD

365 D in a Y

60 M in an H

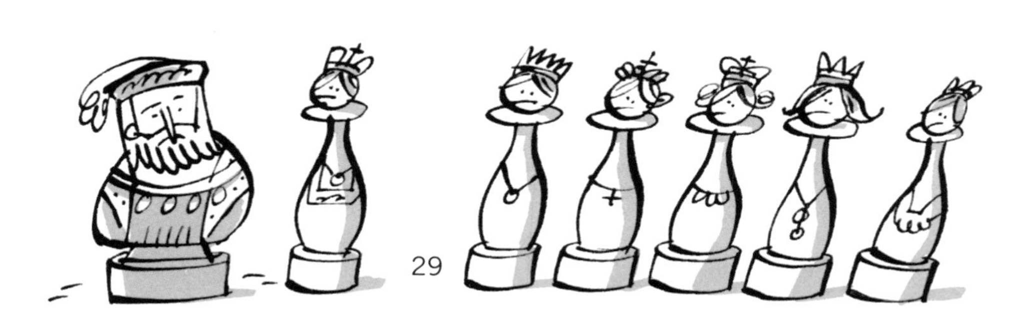

More Homophones

Can you find the homophones that fit the clues below?

C ______ A pleasant journey on a ship

______ People working on yachts in a harbour

M ______ A labyrinth

______ Tall corn plant with large seed on cobs

B ______ Naked

______ Large animal with thick fur, often found in mountains

S ______ Fashion or elegance

______ Wooden structure that helps people climb over fences

B ______ A floating marker placed offshore to mark a channel or hidden rocks

______ A male child

M

A band of fibrous tissue that contracts and relaxes to help your body move

A black shellfish

C

The route something travels (e.g. a river or race track)

Rough, not smooth

P

Jack and Jill went up the hill to fetch one of these

Not bright in colour

P

A time when there is no war

A part or portion of something

Q

Landing place for ships

K

Metal object shaped to open a lock

History: Easy as ABC!

A ....
The most famous Anglo-Saxon king. He was called 'Great' even though he allegedly burnt the cakes

B ....
The sport that Sir Francis Drake was supposedly playing when the Spanish Armada was approaching Britain

C ....
The place where Thomas Becket became a martyr

D ....
English naturalist who wrote *On the Origin of Species* – his theory of evolution

E ....
Saintly king who died in 1066, prompting the Norman invasion

F ....
Ten-week war in 1982 between the UK and Argentina over some islands in the South Atlantic Ocean

G ....
The ship Sir Francis Drake used to circumnavigate the globe in the 16th century

H ....
The most northern frontier of the Roman Empire for nearly 300 years, built on the orders of this emperor in 122 AD

I ....

Civilisation responsible for building Machu Picchu in Peru

J ....

Geological period of time which saw the rise of the dinosaurs and the first birds

K ....

The volcano that made the loudest sound ever heard in modern history when it erupted in 1883

L ....

The city where, in 1666, a fire destroyed thousands of houses but killed fewer than 10 people

M ....

One of the most important documents in history, signed by King John in 1215

N ....

Nurse who went to the Crimean War and was the founder of modern nursing

O ....

Egyptian god of the afterlife

P ....

Greek god of the sea

Q .... Where a medieval archer would have stored his arrows

R .... This was discovered in 1799 and helped historians to decipher Egyptian hieroglyphs

S .... Greek philosopher who was sentenced to death by drinking hemlock

T .... Admiral Horatio Nelson was fatally wounded in this battle in 1805

U .... A form of rain protection probably designed in China

V .... Viking heaven

W .... The place where Chaucer is buried

X .... Musical instrument that gets its name from the Greek words for *wood* and *sound*

Y .... Richard III was the last king from this house

Z .... The king of the gods in Greek mythology

More Divisibility Rules

Work out which boxes you should tick for the numbers on the left. The first one has been done for you. Check your answers with a calculator.

÷	6	7	8	9
336	✓	✓	✓	
60				
180				
343				
216				
882				
392				
368				
459				
154				

Look at the Divisibility Rules (p. 22) if you need help remembering!

Compound Words 2

Find the words that will end the first word and start the second. When you have completed the grid, the shaded squares will reveal the answer to the clue at the bottom of the page.

In her book, *A Room of One's Own*, Virginia Woolf wrote:

"One cannot think well, love well, ______ ______, if one has not dined well."

The English language uses many Greek and Latin prefixes.
bi– is derived from Latin while *di–* comes from Greek.
Can you solve these clues using the prefixes *bi* and *di*?

Double Trouble

A vehicle with two wheels:

____

A chemical compound including two oxygen atoms:

____

This happens twice a year:

____

Optical instrument with a lens for each eye for viewing distant objects:

____

Animal that walks on two feet:

____

An aircraft with two pairs of wings:

____

A situation that requires a choice between two alternatives:

____

To split into two parts – often done with a set of compasses in maths:

____

Someone who speaks two languages:

____

Race of All Time

Not all the competitors in the *Race of All Time* were up to the challenge.

Put ticks and crosses in the grid below to work out what each of the competitors was wearing, what happened to them during the race and where they finished.

	String vest	Hot pants	All-in-one	Jumpsuit	Injured	Went to tavern	Fainted	Shortcut	Winner	Still running	Did not finish	Disqualified
Anne Boleyn				✗								
Captain Scott				✗								
Boudicca	✗	✗	✗	✓								
Einstein				✗								
Winner												
Still running												
Did not finish												
Disqualified												
Injured												
Went to tavern												
Fainted												
Shortcut												

Boudicca wore a pink jumpsuit she stole from the Roman army.

Captain Scott found the weather too hot and did not finish, fainting in front of his wife just as he was about to cross the line.

The competitor wearing hot pants hadn't eaten enough lunch and stopped for a drink and a sandwich in the tavern *en route*.

The winning competitor finished first despite injuring his ankle just after halfway.

The competitor who didn't finish was wearing a leopardskin all-in-one outfit.

The lady who sneakily cheated by taking a shortcut was disqualified — this was not Anne Boleyn.

Anne Boleyn did not wear an old string vest.

Competitor	Wearing	What happened	Position
Anne Boleyn			
Captain Scott			
Boudicca	Jumpsuit		
Einstein			

More Who's Who...

Famous children's author who wrote about a giant peach

Polish scientist and first woman to win a Nobel prize

American computer entrepreneur, inventor, businessman and designer

British woman who led the movement to win the right for women to vote

Dutch painter famous for his sunflowers

Children's author who wrote about a school of witchcraft and wizardry

This man said he would, 'Float like a butterfly, sting like a bee!'

The first woman pilot to fly solo across the Atlantic

Victorian author who wrote about a small boy who wanted more food

19th-century engineer who built ships, bridges and railways.

Figure It Out Again

Albatross

Albert is 36 years old and Ross is 11 years old. In how many years will Albert be twice as old as Ross?

Mathadramatics

Two-fifths of the people sitting in the school theatre are adults. There are 72 adults in the theatre. How many children are there?

Adam's Apple

Adam spends 95p on an apple and an orange. The orange costs 15p more than the apple. How much is the apple?

Spiky Spiders and Flaky Flies

In the heart of the rainforest, Ben the biologist discovers two new species: spiky spiders and flaky flies. Each spider has 26 eyes and each fly has eight.

Ben has caught 50 specimens in his net and in total there are 526 eyes. How many spiky spiders are there in his net?

CU @ The Finish Line

I am running in the marathon with my friends Dart, Sprint, Dash and Flash.

Dart is wearing a three-figure number divisible by 11 which starts with 47...

Dash is wearing a three-figure number that is divisible by 13 and is the same upside down as the right way up.

Sprint is wearing the 30th prime number because it is his birthday today and he asked for it.

Flash is wearing the largest cube number under 1000.

My name is Saunter and I am wearing all of their numbers added together which also happens to be the year I finished school.

What are our numbers, and when did I finish school?

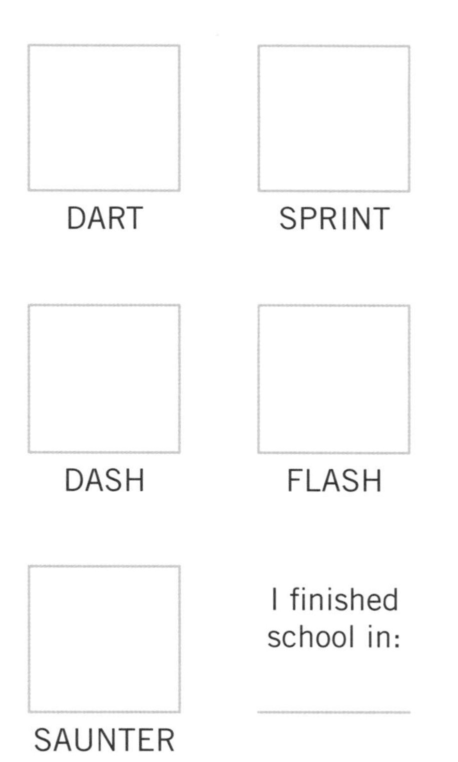

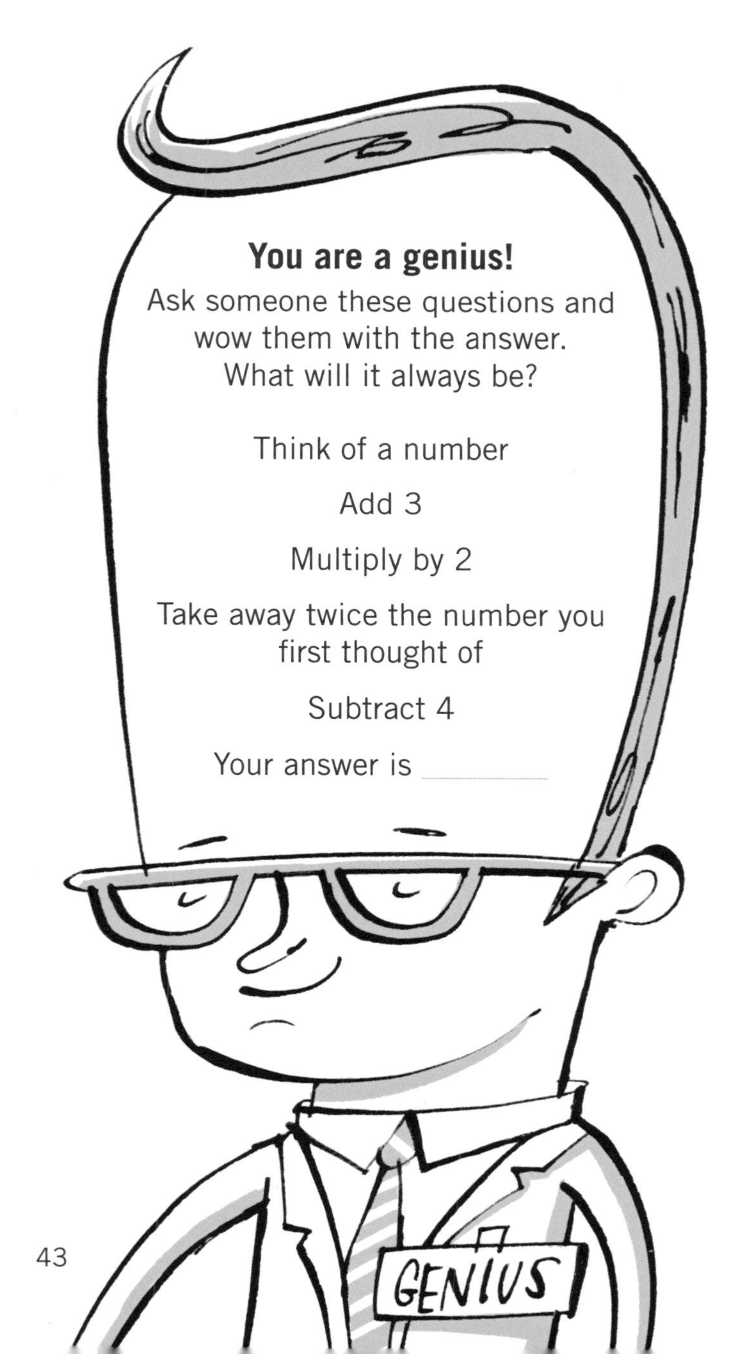

You are a genius!

Ask someone these questions and wow them with the answer. What will it always be?

Think of a number

Add 3

Multiply by 2

Take away twice the number you first thought of

Subtract 4

Your answer is ______

Literary Techniques

When you are answering comprehension questions, you need to be able to identify certain techniques such as alliteration and metaphor.

Solve the clues to complete the crossword using the word bank.

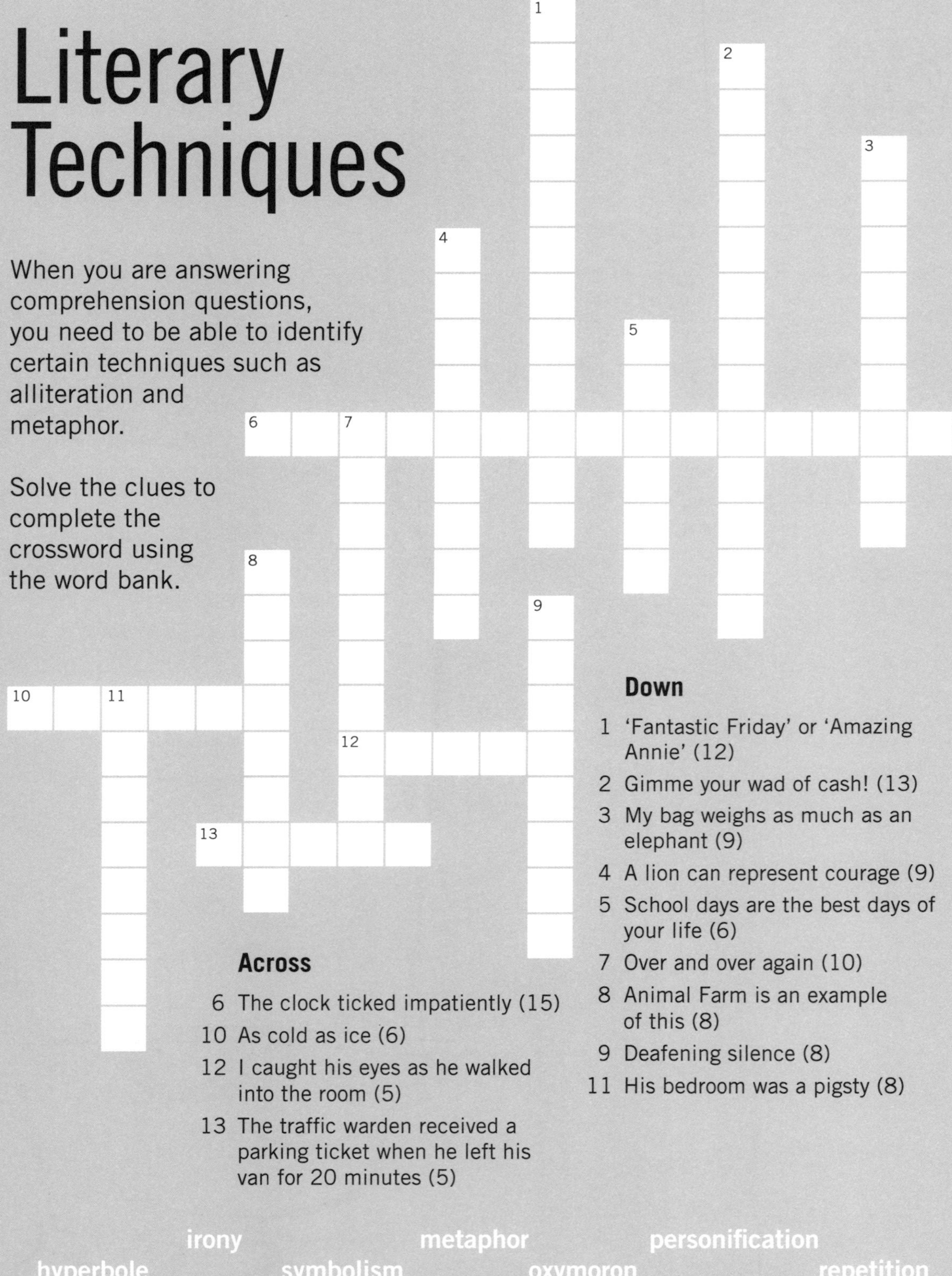

Across

6 The clock ticked impatiently (15)

10 As cold as ice (6)

12 I caught his eyes as he walked into the room (5)

13 The traffic warden received a parking ticket when he left his van for 20 minutes (5)

Down

1 'Fantastic Friday' or 'Amazing Annie' (12)

2 Gimme your wad of cash! (13)

3 My bag weighs as much as an elephant (9)

4 A lion can represent courage (9)

5 School days are the best days of your life (6)

7 Over and over again (10)

8 Animal Farm is an example of this (8)

9 Deafening silence (8)

11 His bedroom was a pigsty (8)

irony metaphor personification
hyperbole symbolism oxymoron repetition
allegory cliché alliteration
idiom colloquialism simile

Geography A to Z

A ____________ Largest state in the USA

B ____________ Highest mountain in the UK

C ____________ Lines joining places of equal height on a map

D ____________ Barren area of dry land, hot or cold, where it is hard for animals to live and plants to grow

E ____________ Imaginary line around the Earth

F ____________ An overflow of a large amount of water beyond its normal limits, especially over what is normally dry land

G ____________ The study of the Earth's surface and the rocks that compose it

H ____________ Severe tropical storm with low pressure and heavy rainfall which can cause extreme damage

I	______________	Large floating mass of ice with nine tenths hidden beneath the surface
J	______________	One of the Channel Islands
K	______________	Country whose capital is Nairobi
L	______________	Capital of Peru
M	______________	Molten rock beneath the Earth's surface
N	______________	The part of the Earth that is north of the equator
O	______________	Scandinavian capital city whose name begins and ends with the same letter
P	______________	City where you find the Eiffel tower
Q	______________	The only country in the world that begins with this letter
R	______________	Turning waste materials into something useful that can be used again

S ______________________ Longest river in the UK

T ______________________ Very large wave caused by an earthquake on the ocean floor

U ______________________ Relating to or in a city

V ______________________ Mountainous vent in the Earth's crust – can spew out lava, ashes, and hot gases from deep inside the Earth

W ______________________ Continuous recycling of water between the sea, air and land

X ______________________ Pirates often leave a map with instructions on where to find the treasure! The phrase is …

Y ______________________ Middle Eastern country near Saudi Arabia and Oman

Z ______________________ Six-lettered landlocked country in Africa

What Comes Next 2?

Fill in the missing numbers in the sequences below.
Most of these follow mathematical rules but the last two require lateral thinking.

1	3	6	10	15					
0	1	1	2	3	5	8	13		
100	99.5	98.5	97	95	92.5				
1	8	27	64						
61	51	43	37	33					
1	4	8	11	15					
–2	4	–8	16	–32					
1	7	6	13	12	20	19			
31	28	31	30	31	30				
3.	1	4	1	5		=			

More Magic Squares

These magic squares have negative numbers, but they still work on the same principle as the magic squares you have already met: all the rows, columns and diagonals add up to the same total. Find the magic totals and solve the squares.

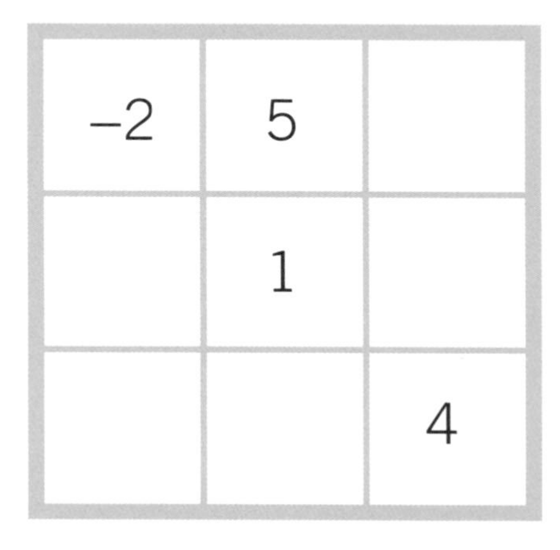

–2	5	
	1	
		4

Magic Total

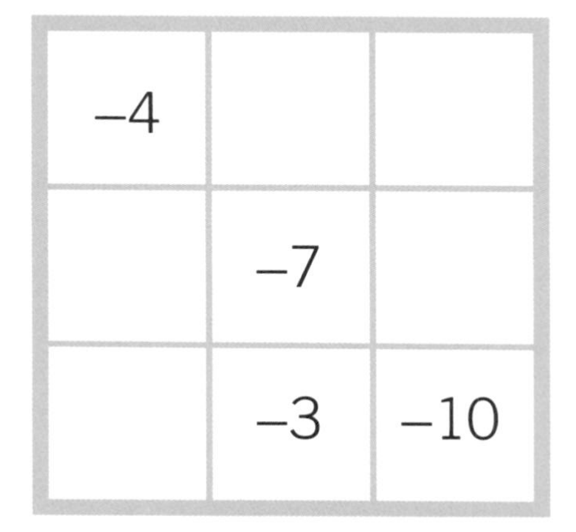

–4		
	–7	
	–3	–10

Magic Total

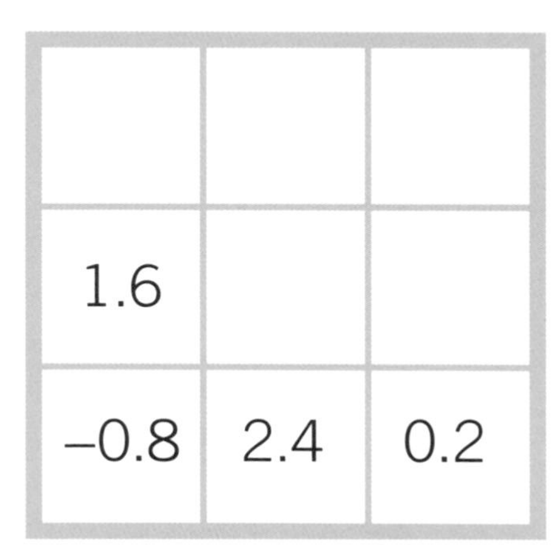

1.6		
–0.8	2.4	0.2

Magic Total

Did you notice the magic total is still three times the number in the centre of the square?

Scrambled Cities

Can you unscramble these UK cities and place them on the map?

NERVINESS	____________	1
A BEER END	____________	2
BEHIND RUG	____________	3
LADS END RUN	____________	4
SAME TRENCH	____________	5
FISHED ELF	____________	6
NON POLLUTING HUSK	____________	7
GIANT MONTH	____________	8
SWARTHY BYTE	____________	9
HI MR BIG MAN	____________	10
CORNY VET	____________	11
GRAINED	____________	12
NON OLD	____________	13
SNAKIEST BOG	____________	14
HOT LUMPY	____________	15
HAM UPON TOAST	____________	16
NIGHT ORB	____________	17

1
2
3
4
5
6
7
8
9
10
11
12
13
14
15
16
17

More Oxymorons

Match up the words below to make an oxymoron:

COLD	UGLY
LIQUID	ELEPHANT
PRETTY	WHISPER
LEAD	KNIFE
DARKLY	YOUNGER
CLEVER	BALLOON
BLUNT	RAGE
LOUD	SUN
GROWING	DELICIOUS
TINY	FOOL
AWFULLY	BRILLIANT
SILENT	GAS

Why use them?

For dramatic effect, for fun, or just to make you think ...

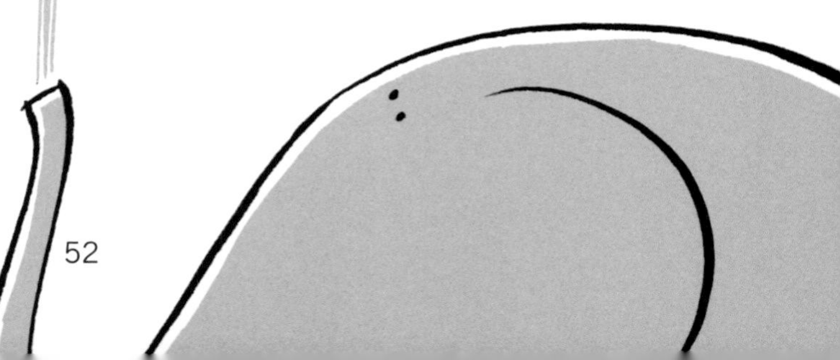

The English prefix *tri–* is derived from both Latin and Greek roots and means:

Three

Can you solve these clues using the prefix *tri–*?

A two-dimensional shape with three sides:

____

A bicycle with three wheels:

____

A three-pronged spear:

____

A group of three stories on the same theme:

____

The large muscle at the back of the upper arm:

____

A stand with three legs to support a camera:

____

A group of three musicians:

____

The skill you have if you speak three languages:

____

A painting made of three panels:

____

Multi-sport event with swimming, cycling and running:

____

Maths is not a Problem

Solve these clues and then find the answers in the word search opposite:

πr^2 is the formula to find the area of a ____________

An angle less than 90º is ____________

A number that is divisible only by itself and 1 ____________

You use this to measure an angle: ____________

When you divide an angle exactly in half you ____________ it

There are 1,000 mm in a ____________

$2\pi r$ or πd gives you the ____________ of a circle

Shapes are ____________ if they are identical to each other in shape and size

1 cm × 1 cm × 1 cm gives you one ____________ centimetre

If you move a shape by sliding it up, down, diagonally or sideways without turning it or changing its size you perform a ____________

A 3-D shape with 12 faces is a ____________

The number on the bottom of a fraction is the ____________

Numbers that follow each other in uninterrupted order are ____________

The ____________ of a circle is the distance across it through the centre

A triangle with three equal angles and three equal sides: ____________

The ____________ of 36 are 1, 2, 3, 4, 6, 9, 12, 18 and 36

The sequence 1 1 2 3 5 8 13 is known as the ____________ sequence

The ____________ is the top number in a fraction

The corner of a shape is its ____________

A 3-D shape with a polygon for its base and triangular faces meeting at one vertex is a ____________

S N N P P R V E F C E U C R T
R N O O R E E I M V V I U O N
O B M I R O B T I I R I D T J
T P I T T O T T E C R I B A C
C V E S N A U R U M M P Q N O
A X T A E C L M A A A B O I N
F J C V E C F S R C E I I M G
X C F S E E T Y N I T I D O R
I Y N R R B P A S A V O S N U
K O T E E T U C A U R Z R E E
C E N C I R C L E G H T C D N
M C U B I C N K K D L U B V T
E N O R D E H A C E D O D O F
Y Z E Q U I L A T E R A L A I
R O T A R E M U N E Y G L R W

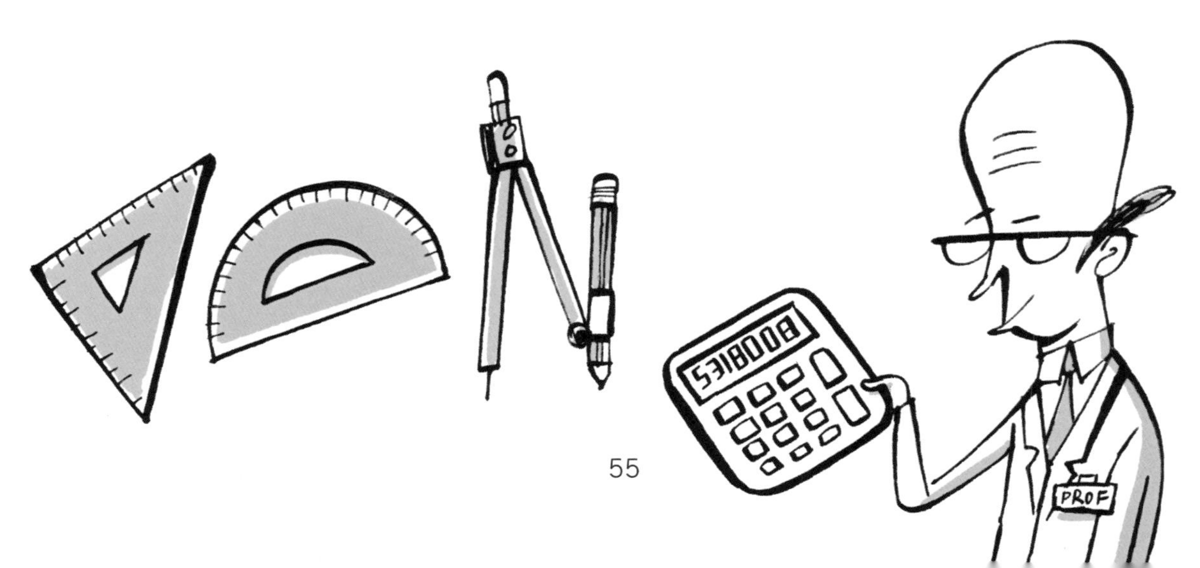

Criss Cross

Across

2 This year, a brood of chickens lays 4008 eggs, which is 502 fewer than last year. How many eggs did they lay last year?

3 The square root of 144

7 The sum of the angles inside a quadrilateral

10 Three hundred and four thousand five hundred and six

11 The number of centimetres in 2 kilometres

12 $5 \times 5 \times 5$

13 How many grams in 8.53 kg?

14 The number of seconds in a day

15 How many litres in 30,000 ml?

Down

1 Pi to 5 decimal places

4 The area of a triangle with height 16 cm and base 32 cm

5 Forty-four thousand, six hundred and ninety-eight

6 The number of minutes in a week

7 The number of days in a year

8 How long in minutes will a car travelling at 50 mph take to travel 60 miles?

9 Eight thousand and eighty-eight

12 The number of metres in a kilometre

The Beginning of the End

Find the two letters which end the first word and start the next...

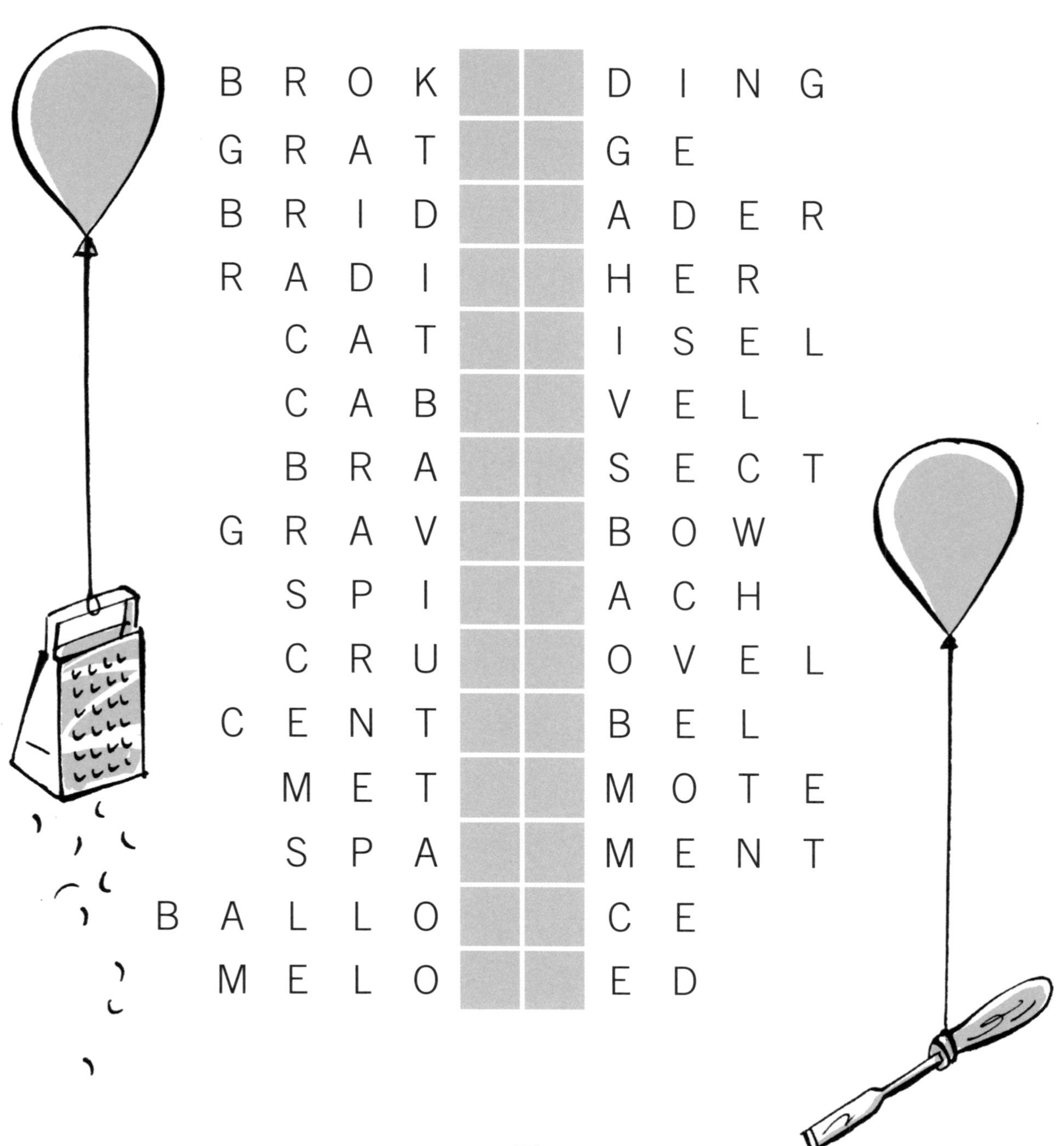

Crack the Code!

We use emojis when writing text messages and emails. They are a modern way of representing thoughts and words using images.

A *rebus* is a type of puzzle that has been popular since the beginning of time. In these puzzles, a word, or part of a word, is represented by a picture, letters or numbers. For example:

Below is a rebus for you to solve with some tips for exam preparation. Can you read the message?

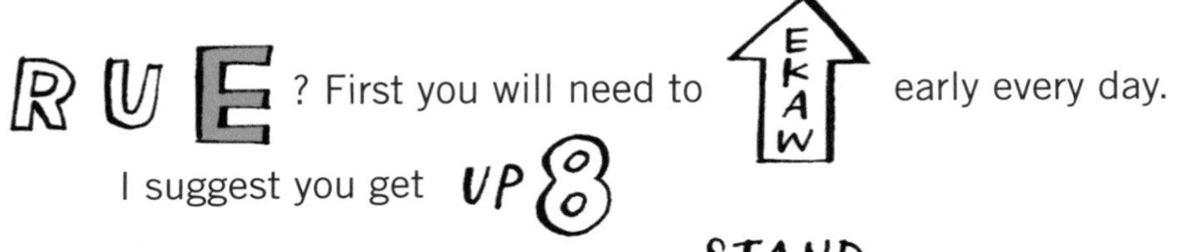

Organise your books and notes and try STAND / 2 all the tricky problems you have encountered along the way.

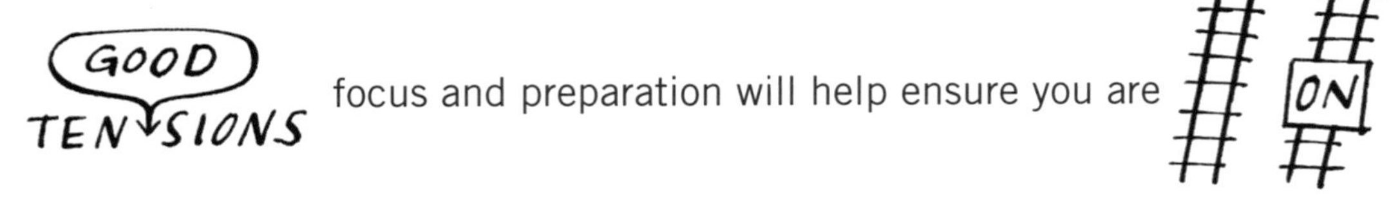

Eat regular meals. Anything will do: proteins, fruit, vegetables, even

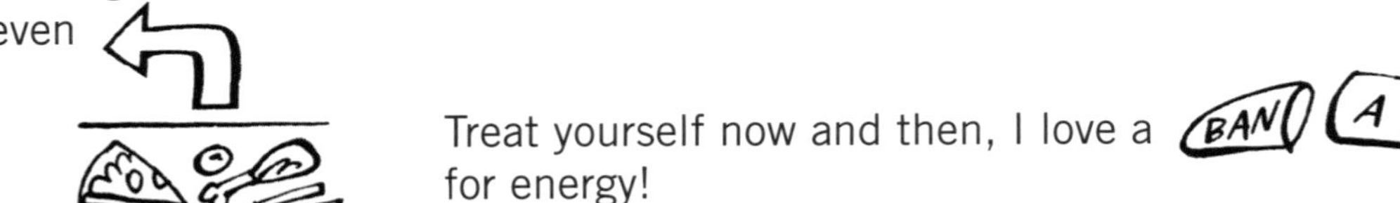

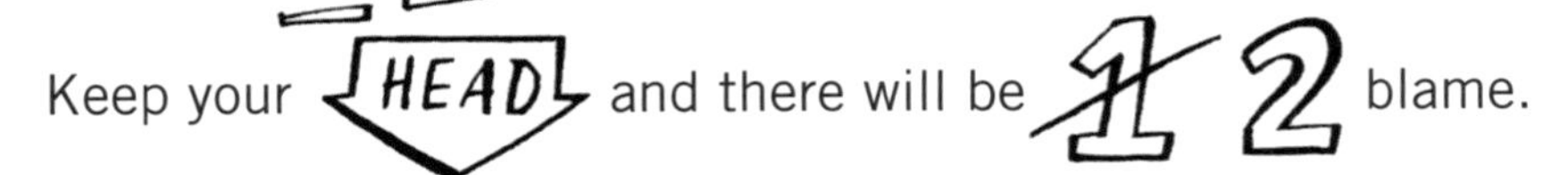

People will admire you and you might even hear them say:

YYUR, YYUB, I C U R YY 4 ME!

Answers

Symbolism and Colour (p. 6)
Red is often associated with passion; blue with cold; green with nature; black with darkness; yellow with sunshine; purple with royalty; grey with something boring; orange with glow; brown with dirt; white with purity.

What Comes Next? (p. 8)
4 8 16 20 24 **28** (+4)
5 10 15 20 25 **30** (+5)
120 105 90 75 60 **45** (–15)
1 2 4 7 11 **16** (+1, +2, +3, +4, +5)
1 4 9 16 25 **36** (1^2, 2^2, 3^2, 4^2, 5^2, 6^2)
100 94 88 82 76 **70** (-6)
3 6 9 12 15 **18** (+3)
3 6 11 18 27 **38** (+3, +5, +7, +9, +11)
–10 –8 –6 –4 **–2** (+2)
5 1 –3 –7 –11 **–15** (–4)

Digit Fidget (p. 9)
24 hours, 30 cm, 330 ml, 16 oz, 1,000 g, 70, 38 plays, 66 books, 10,000 men, 70 mph, 195 countries, 1492, 6 wives, Everest is 8,848 m

Homophones (p. 10)
rain, reign
lesson, lessen
flaw, floor
night, knight
bowls, bowls
berth, birth
medal, meddle
pact, packed
ate, eight

Who's Who? (p. 12)
William Shakespeare, Queen Elizabeth I, Anne Frank, Albert Einstein, Mahatma Gandhi, Sir Winston Churchill, Sir Edmund Hillary & Tenzing Norgay, Rosa Parks, Ludwig van Beethoven

Figure It Out (p. 14)
Life is a bowl of cherries: Professor 40, Peter 36, Susan 45, Edmund 30, Lucy 32. Susan is the hungriest.
Prime Numbers: 13 / Factors: 30
Ten to One: 1 = Atomic number of hydrogen, 2 = The only even prime number, 3 = Number of primary colours, 4 = Four (the only number that contains the same number of letters as its name), 5 = The square root of 25, 6 = Number of sides on a hexagon, 7 = The sum of opposite numbers on a die, 8 = Infinity when turned on its side, 9 = The sum of the digits of any multiple of this number is always this number when reduced to a single digit, 10 = 'X' in Roman numerals

Compound Words (p. 16)
BA**C**K, **H**OUSE, O**U**T, BOA**R**D, BA**C**K, W**H**EEL, DR**I**FT, TAB**L**E, **L**AND = Winston **CHURCHILL**, British Prime Minister from 1940–1945 and from 1951–1955.

Mono (p. 17)
monocle, monolith, monogamy, monopoly, monorail, monologue, monochrome, monosyllable

Science A to Z (p. 18)
Archimedes, Brain, Condensation, Diamond, Electricity, Fossil, Gravity, Heart, Invertebrate, Joint, Kidneys, Liquid, Mammal, Newton, Orbit, Penicillin, Quartz, Roots, Skeleton, Transparent, Uranus, Vertebrate, Water, X rays, Year, Zoology

Bring on the Oxymorons (p. 21)
There are 10: smart casual, deafening silence, paper towel, hot ice, working holiday, plastic glass, virtual reality, bittersweet, living dead, jumbo shrimp

Divisibility Rules (p. 22)

÷	2	3	4	5
12	✓	✓	✓	
60	✓	✓	✓	✓
183		✓		
112	✓		✓	
95				✓
132	✓	✓	✓	
340	✓		✓	✓
364	✓		✓	
7272	✓	✓	✓	
64	✓		✓	

Idioms (p. 24)
1) Sitting on the fence
2) Raining cats and dogs
3) It costs an arm and a leg
4) Let the cat out of the bag
5) Go on a wild goose chase
6) Don't cry over spilt milk
7) Don't count your chickens before they hatch
8) Barking up the wrong tree

Jumper Puzzle (p. 26)
There are 7 gilets, 3 tank tops and 9 fleeces.

Magic Squares (p. 27)

8	3	4
1	5	9
6	7	2

Magic Total 15

0.7	1.4	0.9
1.2	1	0.8
1.1	0.6	1.3

Magic Total 3

8	13	6
7	9	11
12	5	10

Magic Total 27

The magic total is three times the number in the centre of the square.

Think Laterally (p. 28)
24 Hours in a Day
8 Notes in an Octave
6 Wives of Henry VIII
48 Hours in 2 Days
30 centimetres on a Ruler
52 Cards in a Pack (Without Jokers)
6 is Half a Dozen
26 Letters of the Alphabet
7 Wonders of the World
18 Holes on a Golf Course
13 is Unlucky For Some
5 Toes on a Foot
90 Degrees in a Right Angle,
3 Blind Mice (See How They Run!)
11 Players in a Football Team
360 Degrees in a Circle
64 Squares on a Chessboard
13 Loaves in a Baker's Dozen
365 Days in a Year
60 Minutes in an Hour

More Homophones (p. 30)

cruise, crews
maze, maize
bare, bear
style, stile
buoy, boy
muscle, mussel
course, coarse
pail, pale
peace, piece
quay, key

History: Easy as ABC! (p. 32)
Alfred, Bowls, Canterbury, Darwin, Edward the Confessor, Falklands, Golden Hind, Hadrian's Wall, Inca, Jurassic, Krakatoa, London, Magna Carta, Nightingale, Osiris, Poseidon, Quiver, Rosetta Stone, Socrates, Trafalgar, Umbrella, Valhalla, Westminster Abbey, Xylophone, York, Zeus

More Divisibility Rules (p. 35)

÷	6	7	8	9
336	✓	✓	✓	
60	✓			
180	✓			✓
343		✓		
216	✓		✓	✓
882	✓	✓		✓
392		✓	✓	
368			✓	
459				✓
154		✓		

Compound Words 2 (p. 36)
SIDE, SE**L**F, N**E**T, SOM**E**, **P**ORT, **W**ORK, GR**E**EN, **L**IGHT, **L**AND
= **SLEEP WELL**

Double Trouble (p. 37)
bicycle, dioxide, biannual, binoculars, biped, biplane, dilemma, bisect, bilingual

---

Race of All Time (p. 38)

Competitor	Wearing	What happened	Position
Anne Boleyn	Hot pants	Tavern	Still running
Captain Scott	All-in-one	Fainted	Did not finish
Boudicca	Jumpsuit	Shortcut	Disqualified
Einstein	String vest	Injured	Winner

More Who's Who... (p. 40)
Roald Dahl, Marie Curie, Steve Jobs, Emmeline Pankhurst, Vincent Van Gogh, J.K. Rowling, Muhammad Ali, Amelia Earhart, Charles Dickens, Isambard Kingdom Brunel

---

Figure It Out Again (p. 42)
Albatross: Albert will be twice as old as Ross in 14 years. Albert will be 50 and Ross will be 25.
Mathadramatics: 108 children
Adam's Apple: The apple costs 40p (and the orange is 55p)
Spiky Spiders: There are 7 spiky spiders and 43 flaky flies
CU@ The Finish line:
Dart 473, Sprint 113, Dash 689,
Flash 729, Saunter 2004, finished school in 2004
You are a Genius! The answer is always 2

Literary Techniques (p. 44)
1) Alliteration
2) Colloquialism
3) Hyperbole
4) Symbolism
5) Cliché
6) Personification
7) Repetition
8) Allegory
9) Oxymoron
10) Simile
11) Metaphor
12) Idiom
13) Irony

Geography A to Z (p. 45)
Alaska, Ben Nevis, Contours, Desert, Equator, Flood, Geology, Hurricane, Iceberg, Jersey, Kenya, Lima, Magma, Northern hemisphere, Oslo, Paris, Qatar, Recycling, Severn, Tsunami, Urban, Volcano, Water cycle, X marks the spot!, Yemen, Zambia

---

What Comes Next 2? (p. 48)
1 3 6 10 15 **21** (+2, +3, +4, +5, +6)
0 1 1 2 3 5 8 13 **21** (add previous number in sequence)
100 99.5 98.5 97 95 92.5 **89.5** (–0.5, –1, –1.5, –2 etc.)
1 8 27 64 **125** (1^3, 2^3, 3^3, 4^3, 5^3)
61 51 43 37 33 **31** (–10, –8, –6, –4, –2)
1 4 8 11 15 **18** (+3, +4, +3, +4, +3)
–2 4 –8 16 –32 **64** (multiply each number by –2)
1 7 6 13 12 20 19 **28** (+6, –1, +7, –1, +8, –1, +9)
31 28 31 30 31 30 **31** (days of the month in Jan, Feb, Mar etc.)
3 1 4 1 5 **9** ($3.14159 = \pi$)

More Magic Squares (p. 49)

−2	5	0
3	1	−1
2	−3	4

Magic Total 3

−4	−11	−6
−9	−7	−5
−8	−3	−10

Magic Total −21

1	−1.2	2
1.6	0.6	−0.4
−0.8	2.4	0.2

Magic Total 1.8

Scrambled Cities (p. 50)

1. Inverness
2. Aberdeen
3. Edinburgh
4. Sunderland
5. Manchester
6. Sheffield
7. Kingston Upon Hull
8. Nottingham
9. Aberystwyth
10. Birmingham
11. Coventry
12. Reading
13. London
14. Basingstoke
15. Plymouth
16. Southampton
17. Brighton

More Oxymorons (p. 52)

cold sun
liquid gas
pretty ugly
lead balloon
darkly brilliant
clever fool
blunt knife
loud whisper
growing younger
tiny elephant
awfully delicious
silent rage

Three (p. 53)

triangle, tricycle, trident, trilogy, tricep, tripod, trio, trilingual, triptych, triathlon

Maths is not a Problem (p. 54)

Circle, Acute, Prime, Protractor, Bisect, Metre, Circumference, Congruent, Cubic, Translation, Dodecahedron, Denominator, Consecutive, Diameter, Equilateral, Factors, Fibonacci, Numerator, Vertex, Pyramid

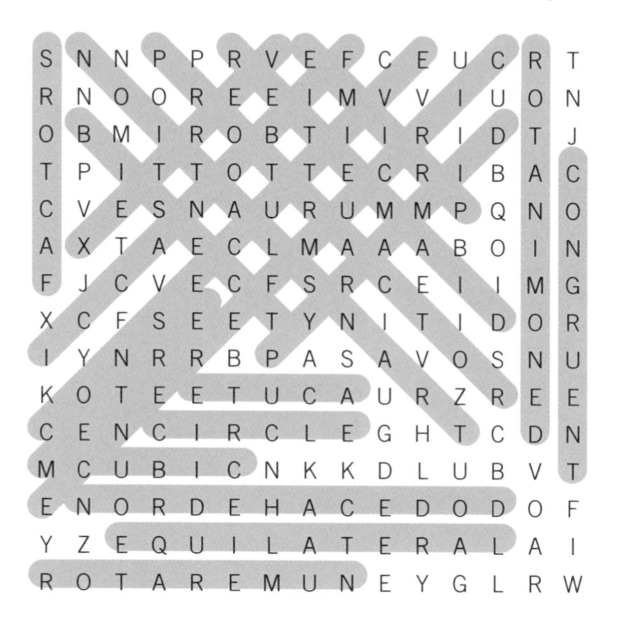

Criss Cross (p. 56)

1) 3.14159
2) 4,510 eggs
3) 12
4) 256 cm^2
5) 44,698
6) 10,080 minutes
7 (across) 360°
7 (down) 365 days
8) 72 minutes
9) 8,088
10) 304,506
11) 200,000 cm
12 (across) 125
12 (down) 1,000 m
13) 8,530 g
14) 86,400 seconds
15) 30 litres

The Beginning of the End (p. 57)

BROK**EN**DING, GRAT**ED**GE, BRID**LE**ADER, RADI**US**HER, CAT**CH**ISEL, CAB**LE**VEL, BRA**IN**SECT, GRAV**EL**BOW, SPI**RE**ACH or SPI**TE**ACH, CRU**SH**OVEL, CENT**RE**BEL, MET**RE**MOTE, BALLO**ON**CE, MELO**DY**ED

Crack the Code! (p. 58)

Are you ready? First you will need to wake up early every day. I suggest you get up before eight. Organise your books and notes and try to understand all the tricky problems you have encountered along the way. Good intentions, focus and preparation will help ensure you are on the right track. Eat regular meals. Anything will do: proteins, fuit, vegetables, even left over food. Treat yourself now and then, I love a banana split for energy! Keep your head down and there will be no one to blame. People will admire you and you might even hear them say: Too wise you are, too wise you be, I see you are too wise for me!

Picture credits

Every reasonable effort has been made to trace the copyright owners for photographs used in this book. If any permissions have been inadvertantly overlooked, the publishers will be pleased to make the necessary changes.

Who's Who? (p. 12) — Albert Einstein (US Library of Congress); Sir Winston Churchill (US Library of Congress); Sir Edmund Hillary & Tenzing Norgay photograph by J. Tenzing Norgay, licensed under Creative Commons; Rosa Parks (US National Archives)

More Who's Who... (p. 40) — Roald Dahl photograph by Hans van Dijk / Anefo (Nationaal Archief Public Domain); Marie Curie (Generalstabens Litografiska Anstalt Stockholm); Steve Jobs by Matthew Yohe, licensed under Creative Commons; Emmeline Pankhurst (US Library of Congress); J.K. Rowling by Daniel Ogren, licensed under Creative Commons; Muhammad Ali World Journal Tribune photo by Ira Rosenberg (US Library of Congress)